Littleland

All Year Round

First published 2015 by Nosy Crow Ltd
The Crow's Nest, 10a Lant Street
London SE1 1QR
www.nosycrow.com.

This edition first published 2016

ISBN 978 0 85763 597 6
Nosy Crow and associated logos are trademarks
and/or registered trademarks of Nosy Crow Ltd

A CIP catalogue record for this book is available from the British Library.

Printed in China by Imago
Papers used by Nosy Crow are made from
wood grown in sustainable forests.

1 3 5 7 9 8 6 4 2

Littleland

All Year Round

Marion Billet

Hello and welcome
to Littleland!
The little ones are going to
nursery on a cold winter morning.
Everyone is happy because there's
so much to do there!
Can you
see...?
lunchbox
bird
squirrel
scarf

But someone is in such
a hurry that they've
dropped their glove.
Can you spot who it is?
flower
scooter
hat
tricycle
helmet

The little ones have arrived at nursery. They hang their coats on their pegs and then they get started!
Can you see...?
globe
bricks
crown
animals

Everyone likes to do different things at nursery. What do you like to do there?

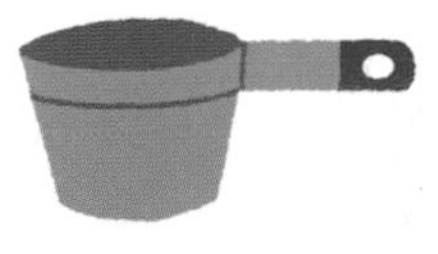

wand pencils jigsaw saucepan clock

On a sunny spring day the little ones love to go to the countryside.
Can you see...?
sheep
watering can
kennel
horse

Can you find ten Easter eggs? That's one egg for every little one!
And can you match the mummy animals to their babies?
cockerel
straw bale
butterfly
wheelbarrow
chick

Where do you think the little ones are now? Yes, they're at a railway station!

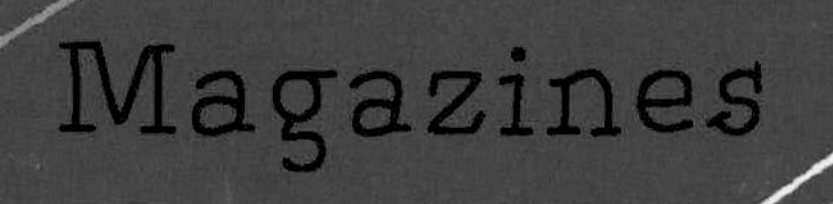

Can you see...?

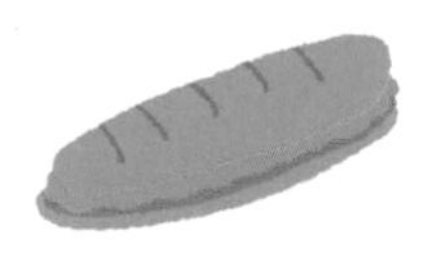

sandwich

lamp

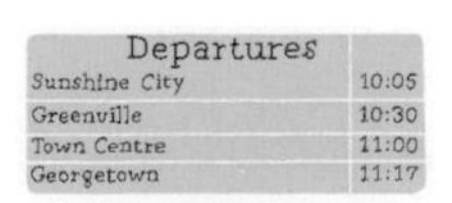

noticeboard

purse

Departures	
Sunshine City	10:05
Greenville	10:30
Town Centre	11:00
Georgetown	11:17

Before they get on the train, the little ones buy their tickets and the things they need for their journey.

train driver

dustbin

ticket

magazine

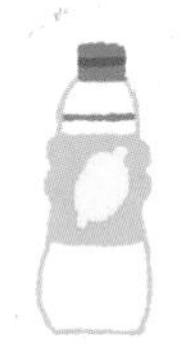
bottle

It’s summertime now, and the little ones have come to their favourite place of all – the seaside!

Can you see…?

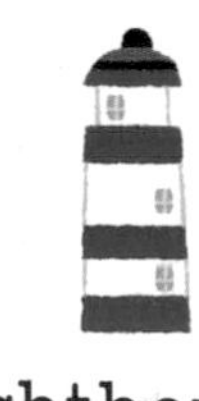

lighthouse

oar

sun lotion

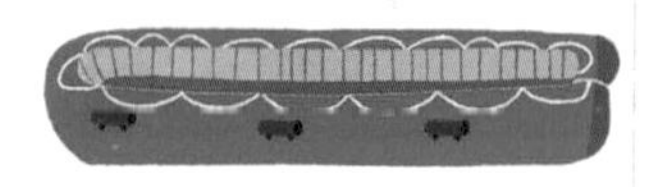

boat

How many fish can you spot in this picture?
crab
fishing rod
starfish
deckchair
fishing net

As a special treat, the little ones have come to the funfair.

Can you see...?

merry-go-round

aeroplane

cart

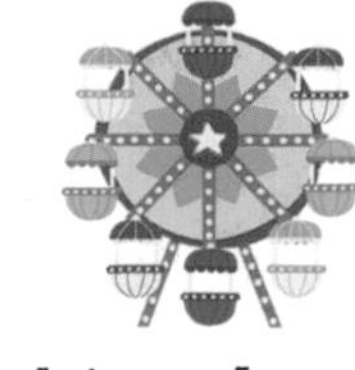

big wheel

They are very excited! Have you ever been to a funfair?

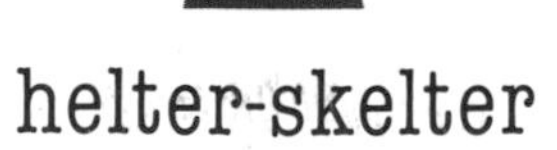

helter-skelter flag star duck balloons

The little ones have come
to their music class now!
Can you see...?
maracas
xylophone
guitar
speaker

Everyone is singing
and dancing. What
a noisy place to be!
blackboard
drum
ring
bell
tambourine

On rainy autumn days the little ones go to the park to play – and to splash in puddles!
They love to feed the ducks!
Can you see...?
umbrella
hedgehog
rainbow
leaf

Do you know all
the colours of
the rainbow?
wellies
rain hat
frog
snail
slide

At Halloween the little ones dress up in costumes and go trick-or-treating! Can you guess who is inside the ghost costume?

Can you see...?

pumpkin

spider

bag

cat

What treat
would you like
to get in your
Halloween basket?
ghost
spider's web
mask
lantern
bone

It snowed last night in Littleland so the little ones are very happy indeed. They love to have fun in the snow!

The ice is very slippery!
The little ones hold hands
and try not to fall over.

tree

snowman

sledge

spade

bench

The little ones have taken out their paper, scissors and glue and are making decorations for their house.

Have you ever made
a card for someone special?
snowflake
scissors
gift tag
paper chain
sticky tape

At Christmas time the little ones go into the town to see the big Christmas tree and the pretty lights.

What a lovely winter scene!
Happy Christmas, Littleland –
see you next year!

moon

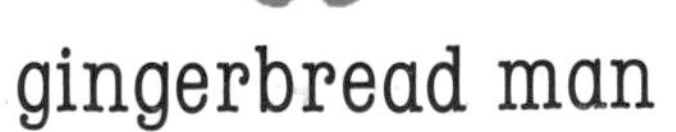

stocking

reindeer

soldier